101 things to do with lutefisk

Ed Fischer gratefully acknowledges the generosity of the Rochester Post-Bulletin, City Pages, and Twin Cities magazine for allowing the reproduction of some of the cartoons in this book.

For additional copies, write
Ed Fischer, 57 Viking Village,
Rochester, MN 55901

Printed by Modern Printers, Faribault, MN
©Ed Fischer 1989
ISBN: 0-9624482-0-6

Cover courtesy City Pages

This book is dedicated to
all fun people, including
Jackie, Pam, Becky, Paula,
and Jessica

LUTEFISK:
Scandinavian dish made from cod soaked in
lye for an extended period of time, or by some
modern, scientific method, and usually
prepared at holidays or on special occasions.
Gets its unique aroma from being cooked.
Sprinkle with warm memories and serve with love.

'...AND HERE'S WHERE THEY KEPT THE LUTEFISK...'

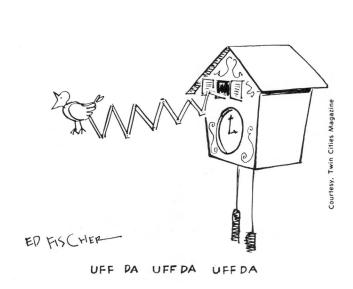

Courtesy, Twin Cities Magazine

Swedes capture Soviet sub in swedish waters
—news item

Alright comrade-talk, or we feed you LUTEFISK!

I'LL TALK! I'LL TALK!

ED FISCHER
ROCHESTER POST-BULLETIN

Courtesy Rochester Post-Bulletin

ED FISCHER

UFF DA UFF DA UFF DA

4

Courtesy Rochester Post-Bulletin

Courtesy Rochester Post-Bulletin

ED FISCHER

Courtesy Twin Cities Magazine

9

'THAT WAS A GREAT IDEA YOU HAD, SVEN - RUBBING
LUTEFISK ON OUR BODIES TO KEEP THE MOSQUITOES AWAY...'

ED FISCHER

Courtesy Rochester Post-Bulletin

11

SMOKING

NON-
SMOKING

ED FISCHER
Courtesy Twin Cities magazine

12

Courtesy Rochester Post-Bulletin

MINNESOTA : LAKES
AND A WHOLE LOT MORE

NINA

ED FISCHER

Courtesy Twin Cities Magazine

101 things to do with lutefisk

Crowd control

PLOP

ED FISCHER

to give to good little Norwegian boys and girls at Christmas

ED FISCHER

lutefisk hockey puck
(won't injure anyone)

ED FISCHER

RADIOACTIVE
AREA
NO LUTEFISK
ALLOWED
(it screws up our
geiger counter)

ED FISCHER

fill for Norwegian pillow

ED FISCHER

mud wrestling

lutefisk wrestling

ED FISCHER

pet lutefisk in a goldfish tank

warmed-up lutefisk

ED FISCHER

ED FISCHER

throw pieces of lutefisk instead of rice at a wedding

ED FISCHER

lutefisk in shoes for a softer walk:

ED FISCHER

frozen lutefisk on a stick

21 flavors!

ED FISCHER

lutefisk as a weed killer

ED FISCHER

a bookmark

ED FISCHER

floating plaything for bathtub

ED FISCHER

pet lutefisk

ED FISCHER

for waking up sleepyheads

ED FISCHER

lutefisk costume
on Halloween

ED FISCHER

really dumb person
trying to catch
lutefisk

ED FISCHER

27

Norwegians stomping lutefisk to make wine

ED FISCHER

lutefisk throwing contest

25

50

ED FISCHER

to get out of school-
put lutefisk into air
conditioning system

ED FISCHER

to attract a
Norwegian wife...

LUTEFISK
after
shave

MUSK

ED FISCHER

for reviving people in comas

ED FISCHER

Cure for the common cold

hang lutefisk around neck

nobody will come near you

ED FISCHER

MOVIE:
Killer
Lutefisk

ED FISCHER

The Christmas
the reindeer
refused to
deliver lutefisk
gifts

ED FISCHER

38

to de-stink
lutefisk

1 rub on deodorant

2 soak in mouthwash

3. Spray with several perfumes

ED ASCHER

for the holidays...
lutefisk
wreath

ED ASCHER

42

take to zoo
and throw at animals
you don't like

ED ASCHER

lutefisk as a
commodity to save

I have 10,000
lutefisks for when
I retire

ED ASCHER

48

lutefisk
hairpiece

ED ASCHER

the mean
witch tries to lure
ole and Ingrid
into the house made
out of lutefisk

ED ASCHER

to clear a
swimming pool
of people

lutefisk
disguised
as steak

SNIFF

to clear
sinuses

Stick
lutefisk
into
each
nostril

ED ASCHEL

Stuff
lutefisk in
ears
(then you won't have to listen
to people making fun of
the lutefisk you're eating

ED ASCHEL

the
pot of
lutefisk
at the end
of the rainbow

ED ASCHER

lutefisk
vending machine

usually placed in
the back of parking lots!

ED ASCHER

lutefisk as birth control

ED FISCHER

emergency lutefisk

ED FISCHER

how to de-stink
lutefisk

1. run over with car

2. place under mattress for a week

3. put in blender

4. Strain through Norwegian flag

ED FISCHER

not recommended—
lutefisk worship

ED FISCHER

lutefisk instead
of
air bags

ED ASCHER

regional lutefisk

Edina: lutefisk under glass

Rochester: lutefisk served in disinfectant

Duluth: Served with smelt (which sounds very appropriate)

ED ASCHER

lutefisk
as a way
to get
someone's
attention...

SPLAT

ED FISCHER

toasted
lutefisk

ED FISCHER

59

emergency lutefisk in Iowa

Break glass

ED ASCHER

lutefisk skirt

ED ASCHER

Storing
lutefisk

ED FISCHER

lutefisk
for
skeet
shooting

ED FISCHER

removing a lutefisk
that has gone really bad...

PLEASE EVACUATE THE AREA

ED FISCHER

WARNING

NEVER EAT LUTEFISK
YOU CAN SEE YOUR FACE IN

ED FISCHER

bringing lutefisk
to the new world...

ED FISCHER

Your idea for something
to do with lutefisk on
this blank page ¿

for lutefisk lovers —
your idea of what can
be done with the cartoonist
of this book ↘